Name: .... Class: ....

KS2 English
SAT Buster

CGP
- books
like no others!

CGP

Spelling
Book 2

Here's what you have to do...

In Year 6 you have to take some tests called the SATs.
This book will help you do well in the spelling bit of the tests.

This is a Spellasaurus — it can spell even the trickiest words.

Your aim is to become a Spellasaurus.

Work through the questions in the book. When you come to a box like this, put a tick to show how you got on.

If you got a lot of spellings wrong, put a tick in the circle on the left. Don't worry — every Spellasaurus has to start somewhere. Make sure you know your spelling rules inside out, then have another go.

If you're nearly there but your spelling is still a bit wobbly, put a tick in the middle circle. Ask your teacher to help you work out the areas you need more practice on.

If you felt really confident and got nearly all the spellings right, tick the circle on the right.

Congratulations — you're a Spellasaurus!

© CGP — not to be photocopied

It's another Quality Book from CGP

This is Book 2 in our KS2 SAT Buster range for Spelling. It's full
of tricky questions to help pupils prepare for the Year 6 SATs.

(The difficulty level is the same as Book 1, so it's perfect for
extra spelling practice — or you can use this book on its own.)

Children can use the Spellasaurus tick boxes for self-assessment,
which helps you work out how they're getting on.

What CGP is all about

Our sole aim here at CGP is to produce the highest quality books
— carefully written, immaculately presented and
dangerously close to being funny.

Then we work our socks off to get them out to you
— at the cheapest possible prices.

Spelling Hints and Tips

Perfecting your spelling is not an easy task, but the hints and tips on this page should help you out. You'll be feeling ready to answer some questions in no time.

1. **Break** the word down into **smaller parts**.

   e.g. mi-cro-phone   ad-ven-ture   po-wer-ful

2. If a word has silent letters, try **pronouncing** it **exactly as you'd spell it**.

   e.g. c-**h**-orus   thum-**b**   **k**-nee

3. **Make up a sentence** to help you remember the word.

   e.g. **design**   **Dirty Elephants Sleep In Giant Nighties**.

4. Look for **smaller words** within the word.

   e.g. at**tent**ion   edu**cat**ion   ca**nd**le   **greed**ily

   Make up a phrase to help you remember how the words are connected.

   e.g. We should have paid more **attention** to our **tent**.

5. If there's a word that you always **struggle** with or get wrong, write it out correctly, and then **copy it out loads of times** until you always get it right without looking.

If you come across a tricky word that you can't think of how to spell, remembering these handy hints could save the day.

1. Think about the **spelling rules** you know.

   e.g. drop the **e** before you add **ing** (e.g. danc**e** — danc**ing**, mak**e** — mak**ing**).

2. Think about words that sound **similar** or that are made from the **same root word**. Maybe your tricky word is spelt in a similar way.

   e.g. **light**, de**light**ed, b**light**   **doubt**, **doubt**ful, un**doubt**edly

3. Write the word in **different ways** — sometimes one way will just **look right**.

   e.g. ~~suprising~~   surprising   ~~serprising~~

© CGP — not to be photocopied

Contents

Published by CGP

Editors
Emma Bonney, Lucy Loveluck, Heather McClelland, Sabrina Robinson
With thanks to Glenn Rogers for the proofreading.

ISBN: 9781782942788
Clipart from Corel®
Printed by Elanders Ltd, Newcastle upon Tyne.
Based on the classic CGP style created by Richard Parsons.

Text, design, layout and original illustrations © Coordination Group Publications Ltd. (CGP) 2014
All rights reserved.

Photocopying this book is not permitted. Extra copies are available from CGP with next day delivery.
0870 750 1242 • www.cgpbooks.co.uk

Section 1 — Word Patterns

Root words

Root words are the main parts of words, which can be used to make lots of other words.

1. Sort the words below into the table according to their root words.

~~unhappy~~   shipped   happiness   unfit

refit   shipment   fittest   happier   shipping

Root word 'happy'	Root word 'ship'	Root word 'fit'
unhappy		

2. Rearrange these jumbled words, and then circle the root word in each one.

    ing   en   deep   ➥   ....(deep)ening.....................

    ed   block   un   ➥   ....

    un   take   able   mis   ➥   ....

    dis   ed   re   cover   ➥   ....

3. Work out the answers to these clues. All of the words have the root word 'press'.

    To make a mark on someone.   __ m __ __ __ s __

    The look on someone's face.   e __ __ __ __ __ __ i __ __

    To keep something back or hold it in.   r __ __ __ __ __ s

    To condense something down.   __ o m __ __ __ __ __

Root words

4. Use the root words in the box to make words to complete the sentences.

| grace | invite | nerve | essence | burglar |

Sunetra sent out party .... to thirty of her friends.

The police said the .... happened at two in the morning.

Robert was feeling very .... before the match.

The ballerina danced .... across the floor.

There's not much room in the car, so we're only packing the ....

5. Write a word containing each of these root words.

help   ....   **load**   ....

back   ....   **argue**   ....

tune   ....   **logic**   ....

6. Think of two different words with the root word **do**, and use each in a sentence.

First word ➡ ....

Sentence: ....

Second word ➡ ....

Sentence: ....

How good are you at going back to your roots?
Tick a box to show how well you did on these pages.

Plurals

Some types of plurals can get tricky, but don't worry — these questions cover 'em all.

1. Write the plural of each word below.

lemon	brick	hamster	dinner
....	....	....	....

2. Tick the plurals which are spelt correctly.
   For those which are incorrect, write the correct plural on the lines.

   a. The island has some lovely **beachs**. ☐ ....*beaches*...............

   b. Fred ate seven **bunches** of grapes. ☐ ....

   c. The **marshs** are scary at night. ☐ ....

   d. We used **torchs** during the power cut. ☐ ....

   e. There are birds living in the **bushes**. ☐ ....

3. Write the plural of each of these words.

   louse ➡ ....   **woman** ➡ ....

   goose ➡ ....   **sheep** ➡ ....

4. Rewrite each sentence using plural nouns.

   a. The **monkey** ate the **cherry**.

   ....

   b. I really liked the **story** about the **fairy**.

   ....

Plurals

5. Circle the plurals that are spelt incorrectly.
   Then write the correct spelling of each incorrect plural in the box.

   (halfs)   cliffs   chefs   themselfs

   sherives   handcuffs   lifes   chiefs

   giraves   brieves   yourselves   wifes

   halves

6. Underline the word in **bold** that has the **correct** spelling in each sentence.

   There are three different (**churchs** / **churches**) in our town.

   I hate the cold, so I went to Jamaica in the Christmas (**holidays** / **holidaies**).

   I like watching (**videos** / **videoes**) of cats on the Internet.

   My gran has some amazing (**memorys** / **memories**) of her childhood.

   We saw lots of (**buffalos** / **buffaloes**) on our safari trip.

7. Write the plural of each of these words in a sentence.

   lunch   ....

   ruby   ....

   igloo   ....

   deer   ....

One Spellasaurus, two Spellasauruses, three Spella...
you get the picture. Tick a box to show how you did.

Double consonants

Words with double consonants can be trickier to <u>spell</u>, so make sure you can recognise them.

1. Complete the words in the sentences by adding a double consonant.

    The man asked my dad to fill out a questio.........aire.

    I do eat vegetables, but only o.........asionally.

    Athletes have to be very co.........i.........ed to their training.

    If there's a fire, you have to leave all your po.........e.........ions behind.

2. Draw a line to join the bits of words together. Write the completed words in the box.

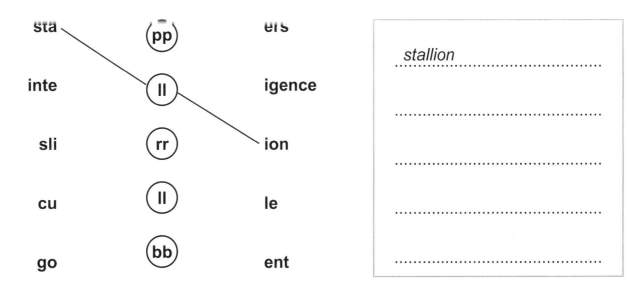

    sta   (pp)   ers

    inte   (ll)   igence

    sli   (rr)   ion

    cu   (ll)   le

    go   (bb)   ent

    stallion ....

    ....

    ....

    ....

    ....

3. **Seven** of the words in the passage below are spelt incorrectly.
    Circle the incorrect words and write the correct spelling of each word in the box below.

    *I try not to be mesy, but it's dificult. My mum gets very cross, and often says she
    will take away my pocket money, but no mater how hard I try my room is always
    teribly untidy. Yesterday, Mum found a roten aple core under my bed. I think it
    might have been there for about a month, because it was prety disgusting.*

Double consonants

4. Use each of these words in a sentence.

    fury   ....

    furry   ....

    of   ....

    off   ....

5. Underline the correct spelling in each sentence below.

    I have asked for a (**buble** / **bubble** / **bubblle**) machine for Christmas.

    The goblin was (**kidnaped** / **kiddnapped** / **kidnapped**) by trolls.

    We've been practising our (**addition** / **addittion** / **adition**) and subtraction.

    Our tree house is (**conected** / **connected** / **conneccted**) to the Internet.

    It's my parents' wedding (**annivversary** / **anniverrsary** / **anniversary**) today.

6. The underlined words are spelt incorrectly. Write the corrections in the boxes.

    Mrs Field was <u>iritated</u> by the <u>gigling</u> at the back of the <u>clasroom</u>.

	giggling	

    I was <u>unsucesful</u>, but I still <u>apreciated</u> the wonderful <u>oportunity</u>.

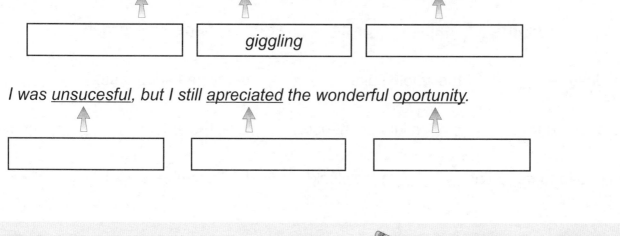

*Spelling words with double consonants is simple
for a <u>Spellasaurus</u>. Have you mastered it yet?*

© CGP — not to be photocopied   *Section 1 — Word Patterns*

The 'ay' sound

1. Circle the correct spelling of each of these words.

    a. **naybour**   **neighbour**   **neabour**

    b. **trade**   **traid**   **trayed**

    c. **paiment**   **payment**   **peament**

    d. **convay**   **conveigh**   **convey**

    e. **chained**   **cheyned**   **chaned**

2. Draw lines to match each word with the correct spelling of the 'ay' sound to fill the gap.

    a g __ __ n s t

    o b __ __

    c r __ __ o n

    | ey |
    | ai |
    | ay |

    d o l __ __ ▪ d

    d r __ __ n p i p e

    t r __ __ n e r s

3. All of these words are spelt incorrectly. Write the correct spelling of each word.

    explane ⇒ ....   **refrean** ⇒ ....

    mistaik ⇒ ....   **sidewase** ⇒ ....

4. Use the words in the box to complete the sentences.

    | eight | pain | grate | ate | pane | great |

    a. Jess .... the whole cake.

    b. We had to .... a kilo of cheese.

    c. I have to get up at .... o'clock.

    d. My pea soup tasted ....

    e. Al broke the .... of glass.

    f. Sid can be such a ....

Are you <u>okay</u> with the 'ay' page? If so, you're well on your <u>way</u> to becoming a Spellasaurus. Tick a box...

Words with 'ough' in

Watch out — the 'ough' spelling can make several different sounds. Time to practise them...

1. Draw lines to link together the words with rhyming 'ough' sounds.

borough		drought		

    | | sought | | | thorough |

    | plough | | | nought | |

2. Underline the correct word to complete each sentence below.

    I always struggle to get the thread (**though / thought / through**) the needle.

    I love strawberry jam, even (**though / thought / through**) I dislike fresh strawberries.

    Katie hated the (**though / thought / through**) of spiders living in her room.

3. Work out the answers to these clues. All of the words contain 'ough'.

    The name for bread mix before it's baked.   ....

    The container farm animals eat from.   ....

    A word meaning 'sufficient' or 'adequate'.   ....

    The past tense form of 'to bring'.   ....

4. Write a sentence using both of the words below.

    fought   tough

    ....

The 'ough' sound can be a little <u>rough</u>, but practice makes perfect. How did you do, young Spellasaurus?

The 'f' sound

1. Tick the words that are spelt correctly.
   For those which are incorrect, write the correct words on the lines.

   a. I picked up the medicine from the **farmacy**. ☐ ....*pharmacy*............

   b. My best **phriend** is called Leyla. ☐ ....

   c. The artist used different shapes for **effect**. ☐ ....

   d. Amir has a **fobia** of enclosed spaces. ☐ ....

   e. My baby brother's room is very **colourful**. ☐ ....

2. Complete the words in the sentences by adding **f** or **ph**.

   a. Marge is my aunt, so I am her ne......ew.

   b. Hannah re......used to do her homework.

   c. I forgot to plot any points on my gra......

   d. P.E. means ......ysical education.

   e. This micro......one is rubbish.

   f. My favourite science is ......ysics.

3. Complete this table by filling in the missing words with the 'f' sound.

Word	Clue
a _ o _ _ _ _ _ _	a punctuation mark used to show missing letters
d _ _ _ _ t	to beat someone in a competition
p a _ _ _ _ _ _ _	a group of sentences
c _ n _ _ _ t	to oppose or challenge someone
t _ _ _ o o _	a very strong tropical storm

This page may have left you _feeling fabulous_, but have you done _enough_ to earn the Spellasaurus _trophy_?

 © CGP — not to be photocopied

Prefixes — im, in, il and ir

Prefixes go at the start of a word — they can completely change its meaning.

1. Add the correct prefix to complete these sentences.

    The judge is very fair. She is always ....partial.

    Some dog whistles are ....audible to humans.

    His decision was confusing and ....logical.

    My cat finds spaghetti bolognese ....resistible!

2. Underline the word that has the correct prefix in each sentence.

    Tommy's excuse for not doing his homework was (**irplausible** / **implausible**).

    Sam's letter to Santa was (**inlegible** / **illegible**), so all he received was coal.

    It would be highly (**inpractical** / **impractical**) to make a teapot out of chocolate.

    In her new disguise, the detective tried to remain (**inconspicuous** / **imconspicuous**).

3. Use the prefixes in the box to change the meanings of these root words.

ir	il	in	im

    ....precise   ....regular   ....ability

    ....legitimate   ....replaceable   ....elegant

    Choose one of the words you have made and use it in a sentence.

    ....

Even the most __imperfect__ Spellasaurus can master prefixes with practice. How are you doing?

Prefixes — auto, trans, bi, tri and semi

1. Underline the word that has the correct prefix in each sentence.

   My special skills are looking fabulous and signing (**transgraphs** / **autographs**).

   The astronauts set the rocket to (**autopilot** / **semipilot**) and put their feet up.

   Both teams were desperate to make it through to the (**semifinals** / **trifinals**).

   People should see the dentist (**biannually** / **transannually**), or twice a year.

2. Draw lines to match the correct prefix to the root words.
   Write the completed words in the box.

   auto   circle

   trans   port   *automobile*

   bi   mobile

   tri   plane

   semi   angle

3. Complete the words in these sentences using the prefix **auto**, **trans**, **bi**, **tri** or **semi**.

   I wish I could ....form all vegetables into chocolate.

   Sue said the storyline is about her life — it's an ....biographical film.

   Children may ride a ....cycle before they learn to ride a ....cycle.

   My grandad is ....retired — he only works part-time these days.

   We're ....planting the tomato plants from the greenhouse to the garden.

How did you find those prefixes, young Spellasaurus?
Tick to show how you think you did on this page.

Prefixes – aero, micro, super, sub, inter

1. Circle the words that have the wrong prefix.

   Write the correct spelling of each incorrect word in the box — they should begin with either **aero**, **micro**, **super**, **sub** or **inter**.

(intermodel)	microphone	aeroactive	microplane
interwave	aeromerge	aerodrome	superheading

   supermodel

2. Add the prefix **aero**, **micro**, **super**, **sub** or **inter** to each of these root words.

   ....dynamic   ....locking

   ....market   ....total

   ....scope   ....vision

   ....marine   ....glue

3. Add the prefix **aero**, **micro**, **super**, **sub** or **inter** to each word and use the new word in a sentence.

   chip   *A **micro**chip in a computer can store lots of information.* ....

   natural   ....

   way   ....

   national ....

Spellasauruses are <u>international</u> spelling <u>superheroes</u>.
Draw a tick to show how super you are at prefixes.

Section 2 — Word Beginnings

Prefixes — tele, mis, anti, photo, circum

1. Add the prefix **tele**, **mis**, **anti**, **photo** or **circum** to complete each sentence.

The fluffy, green alien felt like a bit of a ....fit down on earth.

The popstar's concert was ....vised live from the stadium in London.

She cleaned the cut with ....septic liquid and put a plaster on it.

The scientist peered through his powerful ....scope and admired the stars.

The ....ference of the circle measured 10 cm.

2. Add the prefix **tele**, **mis**, **anti**, **photo** or **circum** to each of these root words.

................graph   ....stance   ....clockwise

................phone   ....spell   ....social

................biotic   ....guided   ....navigate

3. Tick the words that are spelt correctly.
For those which are incorrect, write the correct words on the lines.

a. The **televirus** software isn't working.   ☐   *antivirus* ....

b. The evidence was purely **circumstantial**.   ☐   ....

c. I **photodialled** the telephone number.   ☐   ....

d. My sister cried when the **misvision** broke.   ☐   ....

e. Ben took an **anticopy** of his certificate.   ☐   ....

f. Frank **mispronounced** my name.   ☐   ....

If you're not underlined{misspelling} words with prefixes, you're doing well. Give us a tick to show how you're doing.

Hyphenating prefixes

Some words always need a hyphen. Other times, a word can have two different meanings depending on if it has a hyphen or not. Spellasauruses know which words need hyphens.

1. Draw lines to join each prefix to the correct word.

    Write the completed words in the box. All the words need a hyphen.

(ex)	wife	ex-wife
	belief	
(self)	stick	
	mayor	
(non)	country	
	toxic	
(cross)	portrait	
	eyed	

2. Write the words below in the correct place in the table.

    re-mark   **remark**   **re-sign**   **resign**   **re-treat**   **retreat**

Word	Definition
....	To mention or say something.
....	To treat someone again.
....	To quit your job.
....	To sign something again.
....	To mark something again.
....	To pull back or back down.

Did those tricksy hyphens get the better of you?
Draw a tick to show how well you think you did.

© CGP — not to be photocopied

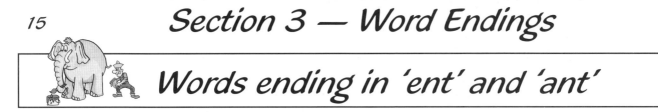

Section 3 — Word Endings

Words ending in 'ent' and 'ant'

Getting word beginnings right is great, but we need to sort out word endings too.

1. Complete this table by adding **ent** or **ant** to the words in the box.

Ends in ent	Ends in ant
....	....
....	....
....	....
....	....

urg

gi

viol

observ

assist

innoc

rec

pheas

2. Underline the word in **bold** that has the correct ending in each sentence.

   Eva loves Spain and she makes (**frequent** / **frequant**) trips to Madrid.

   The visitors thought the artwork was simply (**magnificant** / **magnificent**).

   Robbie wants to be an (**accountent** / **accountant**) when he grows up.

   Catherine complained that she hadn't had a (**decent** / **decant**) cup of tea in a long time.

3. Complete the words in this passage using **ent** or **ant**.

   After a disagreem........ about what the school play should be about, the pupils finally decided on a theme and there was a lot of excitem........ in the hall. When the import........ auditions took place, some pupils were reluct........ to take part, but others were confid........ they would be given a role. Jane was hesit........ as she approached the expect........ teachers, but after a short mom........, she began to sing beautifully.

It's funny how 'ent' and 'ant' can sometimes sound the same. Tick a box to show how well you can spot this.

   © CGP — not to be photocopied

Words ending in 'ence' and 'ance'

1. Add **ence** or **ance** to complete the following words.

    guid........................   abs........................   ambul........................

    innoc........................   fragr........................   toler........................

    insur........................   reli........................   intellig........................

2. Add **ence** or **ance** to complete these words, and then use each of them in a sentence.

    resid ....

    occurr ....

    appli ....

    acquaint ....

    exist ....

3. One word in each of the sentences below is spelt incorrectly.
   Circle the mistake and write the word out correctly on the line.

   Snuffles, my dog, attends (obediance) classes. ....*obedience*..............

   She danced across the room with such elegence. ....

   Erin has more independance, thanks to her new car. ....

   I cannot understand the relevence of this discussion. ....

   The show was great, but the audiance didn't turn up. ....

   The numbers must be entered in a specific seqance. ....

Have you answered all the questions? Are you sure? Then tick a box to show how well you did on this page.

Words ending in 'cial' and 'tial'

The best way to crack these tricky endings is practice, practice, practice. So, let's get going...

1. Complete the words in these sentences by adding **cial** or **tial**.

    The police are trying to stop antiso.................. behaviour.

    Preparations are being made for the next presiden.................. election.

    Kelly doesn't think it's fair that Rebecca gets preferen.................. treatment.

    Judo is a mar.................. art which originates from Japan.

    During the storm, our house only suffered superfi.................. damage.

2. Draw lines to join each word to the right ending.
    Write the completed words in the box.

    influen
    unsubstan
    provin
    sacrifi
    residen
    offi

    (cial)

    (tial)

    influential

3. Add **cial** or **tial** to the end of each of these words and use the word in a sentence.

    impar   *Jason needed some impartial advice on how to invest his money.*

    artifi   ....

    ini   ....

    commer   ....

It's great to be a Spellasaurus. Are you on your way to becoming a big Spellasaurus? Tick to show your level.

Words ending in 'cious' and 'tious'

The word endings on this page are simply deli<u>cious</u>. You'll gobble them up in no time at all.

1. Circle the words that are spelt incorrectly.
   Write the correct spelling of each incorrect word in the box.

   (lustious)   ungratious   contentious   pretencious

   vivacious   vitious   spatious   malicious

   luscious

2. Underline the word in **bold** that has the correct ending in each sentence.

   Some people thought that flying to the Moon was (**overambitious** / **overambicious**).

   Richard's doughnuts looked very (**scrumpcious** / **scrumptious**).

   Kareem is pleased to hear his illness is not (**infectious** / **infeccious**).

   The man outside the bakery looked very (**suspitious** / **suspicious**).

   Fruit and vegetables are said to be very (**nutricious** / **nutritious**).

3. Complete the words in this passage by adding **cious** or **tious**.

   > *Calvin thinks Viv is overcau.................. when it comes to running. Before going for a jog, she wraps her knees and elbows in bubble wrap because she says her joints are pre.................. Viv's also a bit supersti.................., so she takes a four-leaf clover along for luck. She thinks it works because when a fero.................. dog approached her, she managed to shoo it away.*

*Some words on this page are as long as a
Spellasaurus's tail. How did you find them?*

© CGP — not to be photocopied   *Section 3 — Word Endings*

Words ending in 'able' and 'ible'

Word endings sometimes sound similar, but are spelt differently. Watch out for these.

1. Add **able** or **ible** to complete each of the following words.

    collect.................................

    accept.................................

    applic.................................

    advis.................................

    leg ....

    ined.................................

    flex ....

    remark.................................

2. Circle the words that are spelt incorrectly.
    Write the correct spelling of each incorrect word in the box.

    (horrable)   enjoyable   miserible   accessible

    reasonible   comfortable   questionible   considerible

horrible

3. Add **able** or **ible** to the end of each of these words and use the word in a sentence.

    adjust   *Dad was pleased with the car's new adjust**able** sunroof.*...............

    respons ....

    change ....

    invis ....

Only one letter makes 'able' different from 'ible'. Tick to show how confident you are with these endings.

        © CGP — not to be photocopied

Words ending in 'al', 'el' and 'le'

1. Underline the word in **bold** that has the correct ending in each sentence.

   Helen reuses her tea bags — she likes to be (**economicel** / **economical**).

   Lauren hurt her arm on a stinging (**nettle** / **nettel**) by the lake.

   My uncle has an (**originle** / **original**) SuperCats comic from 1957.

   When we're in Egypt, we plan to have a ride on a (**camle** / **camel**) across the desert.

2. Complete this table by adding **al**, **el** or **le** to the words in the boxes.

   | anim | typic | artic | flann | ab | vess | barr | person | wrink |

Ends in al	Ends in el	Ends in le
....	....	....
....	....	....
....	....	....

3. Complete the words in these sentences using **al**, **el** or **le**.

   Marcus had to canc.................. his holiday because he was ill.

   The warriors attacked the cast.................. and took the princess hostage.

   Treacle pudding is a good examp.................. of a traditional dessert.

   The gener.................. ordered his troops to retreat to the river.

A Spellasaurus knows the difference between 'al', 'el' and 'le' endings. How well did you do on this page?

© CGP — not to be photocopied

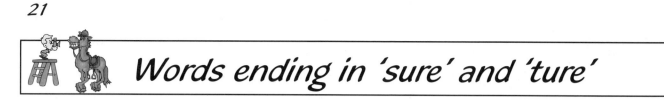

Words ending in 'sure' and 'ture'

Keep your compo<u>sure</u> on this page and make <u>sure</u> you can use 'sure' and 'ture' correctly.

1. Draw lines to join each word to the right ending.
   Write the completed words in the box.

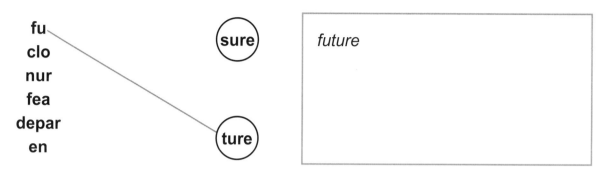

2. Underline the word in **bold** that has the correct ending in each sentence.

   Sarah didn't dare (**vensure** / **venture**) outside during the snowstorm.

   The zookeeper tried to (**reassure** / **reasture**) the visitors that the lion was friendly.

   Louise thought that giving up chocolate was a form of (**torsure** / **torture**).

3. Use the clues to write words that end in **sure** or **ture**.

   Another word for farming.   a...........................

   Something you might hang on your wall.   p...........................

   Pirates go in search of this.   t...........................

   Books and magazines are examples of ...   l...........................

   A feeling of being displeased.   d...........................

   A funny cartoon drawing of someone.   c...........................

How <u>sure</u> are you that you know when to use 'sure' and when to use 'ture'? Pick a box and give it a tick.

                    © CGP — not to be photocopied

Words ending with a 'shun' sound

1. Complete this table by adding **sion** or **tion** to the words in the box.

Ends in sion	Ends in tion
....	....
....	....
....	....
....	....

man

ac

colli

inten

intru

reduc

fric

expan

2. Add **tion** or **cian** to the end of each of these words and use the word in a sentence.

clini   *I went to see the clinician about my sore throat.*

direc   ....

beauti   ....

opera   ....

3. Circle the words that have the wrong ending.

Write a short paragraph that includes the correct spelling of all the words you've circled.

mathematician   discusion   television   solution   permision

....

....

....

A Spellasaurus finds 'shun' sounds spellbinding. Tick a box to show how spelltacular you find shun endings.

Words ending with 'en' and 'on'

You need to be <u>on</u> the ball with this page. So, thinking caps <u>on</u> and off you go...

1. Add **en** or **on** to complete each of the following words.

    oni....................................   falc....................................

    drag....................................   lem....................................

    elev....................................   flatt....................................

    fright....................................   length....................................

2. Complete this table by adding **en** or **on** to the words in the boxes.

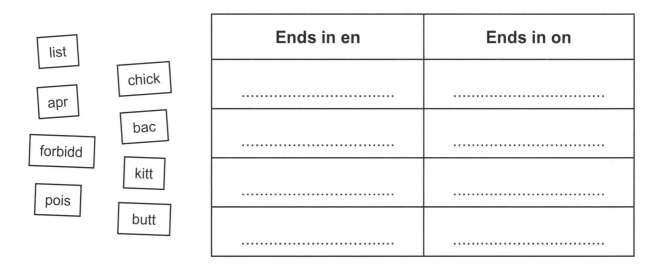

	Ends in en	Ends in on
	....	....
	....	....
	....	....
	....	....

list

apr

forbidd

pois

chick

bac

kitt

butt

3. Use the clues to write words that end in **en** or **on**.

    Spring, summer and autumn are all types of this.   ....

    Police cars use this to warn people they're coming.   ....

    Another word for winner.   ....

    Plants produce this and it can make people sneeze.   ....

Are you a mightily big Spellasaurus after completing this page, or are you still growing? Tick a box.

     © CGP — not to be photocopied

Words ending with 'er' 'ar' and 'or'

1. Complete the words in these sentences using **er**, **ar** or **or**.

   Dylan didn't mean to splash his swimming instruct......

   A burgl...... broke into the house and stole Fiona's guit.......

   The kidnapp...... took the goat belonging to my English tut.......

   Lawrence didn't know the answ...... to his teacher's question.

   The visit...... feared he would be in dang...... if he went out after dark.

2. Draw lines to join each word to the right ending.
   Write the completed words in the box.

   nect

   transf

   angul

   suppli

   particul

   sail

   er

   ar

   or

nectar

3. Add **er**, **ar** or **or** to the end of each of these words and use the word in a sentence.

   cell   *The only safe place for Caroline's chocolate was in the cell**ar**.* ....

   radiat ....

   drumm ....

   caterpill ....

   emper ....

Did you get the hang of 'er', 'ar' and 'or' endings?
They're tricky things. Tick to show how you performed.

Words ending with 'ery' 'ary' and 'ory'

You're over halfway through this section now — just a few more endings to get right.

1. Underline the word in **bold** that has the correct ending in each sentence.

   You have to drive around the (**estuary** / **estuory**) to get from Millom to Barrow.

   Kate says that ice cream is (**obligatary** / **obligatory**) on Sundays.

   Ellen's hat flew off her head in the (**blustery** / **blustary**) wind.

   Lesley had an enormous collection of expensive (**jewellery** / **jewellary**).

2. Draw lines to join each word to the right ending.
   Write the completed words in the box.

qu	(**ery**)
cook	
lavat	(**ary**)
territ	
honor	(**ory**)
mem	

   query

3. Some of the words in the passage below are spelt incorrectly.
   Circle the incorrect words and write the correct version of each word in the box below.

   > In February, Jim and Julie are celebrating their anniversery. Julie wants a party and has planned everything down to the flowary tablecloth. She gave Jim a summory of her ideas. However, Jim thought that an ordinery day would be satisfactary and that fish and chips would be even better.

   February

How easy did you find the questions on this page? Are you a confident Spellasaurus or still a bit shaky?

© CGP — not to be photocopied

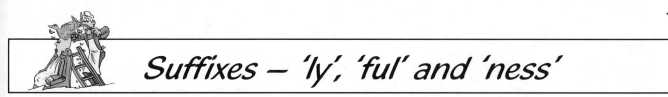

Suffixes – 'ly', 'ful' and 'ness'

If you can add suffixes correctly to root words, you'll have even more words to use. Great!

1. Circle the words that are spelt incorrectly.
    Write the correct spelling of each incorrect word in the box.

    (beautyful)   carefuly   wearyness   extremly

    perfectly   madness   thankfull   grateful

    > *beautiful*

2. Draw lines to join each adjective to the correctly spelt adverb.

    scary   **easy**   **merry**   **weary**   **shy**   **lazy**

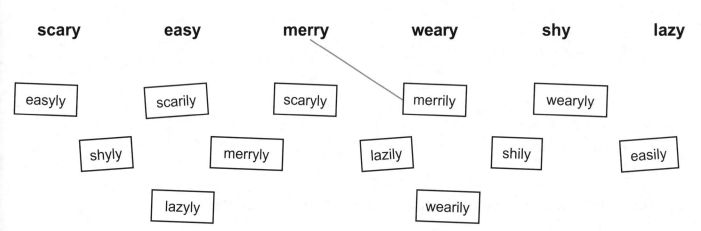

    easyly   scarily   scaryly   merrily   wearyly

    shyly   merryly   lazily   shily   easily

    lazyly   wearily

3. One word in each of the sentences below is spelt incorrectly.
    Circle the mistake and write the word out correctly on the line.

    The teacher said my behaviour was (absolutly) unacceptable. .... *absolutely* ....

    Gareth's gift was very thougtfull, but it wasn't necessary. ....

    "Stop this naughtyness at once!" Mum shouted loudly. ....

    The monster under my bed suffers from lonelyness. ....

Spellings are extra tricky if root words change when you add a suffix. Tick to show how well you did.

© CGP — not to be photocopied   *Section 3 — Word Endings*

Suffixes – 'ing' and 'ed'

Keep your eyes peeled for root words that change when suffixes are added to them.
Dropping the final 'e' before adding the suffix is a particularly sneaky change.

1. Look at these root words and suffixes. Write how the root word must be changed before the suffix is added. Sometimes the root word doesn't need to change.

    a. scrub + ing   ➡ *Double the last consonant.* ....

    b. multiply + ed   ➡ ....

    c. worry + ing   ➡ ....

    d. reconcile + ed   ➡ ....

    e. label + ing   ➡ ....

    f. achieve + ed   ➡ ....

    g. swap + ing   ➡ ....

    h. try + ed   ➡ ....

2. Add the suffix to the root word and write the new word on the line.

    persuade + ing = ...   worship + ing = ...

    omit + ed = ...   announce + ed = ...

    copy + ed = ...   empty + ed = ...

    tunnel + ing = ...   deter + ing = ...

3. Add the suffix **ing** to each word and use the new word in a sentence.

    escape   ....

    cry   ....

          © CGP – not to be photocopied

Suffixes – 'ing' and 'ed'

4. These words are spelt incorrectly. Write the correct version of each word in a sentence.

    perspireing   ....

    swated   ....

    qualyfied   ....

    knited   ....

5. Complete each sentence by filling in the missing word.
    All the missing words end in ing.

    Rupert hated <u>l</u> <u>o</u> __ __ <u>n</u> <u>g</u> – he always wanted to win.

    Ivan is <u>w</u> __ <u>a</u> __ __ <u>i</u> <u>n</u> __ his little sister's birthday present.

    Janet is <u>a</u> <u>p</u> __ __ __ __ <u>n</u> <u>g</u> to university.

    We are <u>m</u> <u>o</u> __ <u>i</u> __ __ house in September.

6. This word search contains 10 words ending
    in 'ed'. Find them and write them in the box.

I	M	P	R	O	V	E	D	R	I	S
R	T	U	D	X	S	Q	D	M	C	T
S	R	E	N	T	A	S	T	E	D	U
U	C	R	R	E	C	E	I	V	E	D
R	L	Y	B	W	E	N	L	H	A	I
P	O	S	Z	T	A	C	A	T	R	E
R	V	P	I	U	B	U	R	I	E	D
I	E	I	P	A	D	U	C	T	I	F
S	D	E	P	F	U	E	L	L	E	D
E	S	D	E	N	Q	U	E	T	U	Z
D	M	J	D	B	U	R	N	Q	E	G

Have you mastered 'ed' and 'ing' endings? Can you tick
the big Spellasaurus or is it one of the other two?

© CGP — not to be photocopied

Suffixes – 'ment', 'ship' and 'hood'

The suffixes on this page don't usually change the root word, but watch out – there are some sneaky exceptions. Don't let them fool you. Practise them and conquer them!

1. Write these root words in the box, adding **ment**, **ship** or **hood** to make new words.

   knight   **merry**   **owner**   **friend**

   knighthood

2. Complete the table using the clues to write words ending with **ment**, **ship** or **hood**.

Word	Clue
t...........................	You might need this if you are ill or injured.
c...........................	The time you spend as a child.
b...........................	A boat that takes part in a war at sea.
a...........................	What Americans call a flat.

3. One word in each of the sentences below is spelt incorrectly.
   Circle the mistake and write the word out correctly on the line.

   Dance lessons can improve your (movemint) skills. ....*movement*............

   The likelyhood that we'll lose is very high. ....

   The science experyment was a complete disaster. ....

   Mr Jeeves prepared breakfast for his lorddship. ....

Sailors love words ending in 'ship' and coats love those ending in 'hood'. How good are you at these endings?

          © CGP — not to be photocopied

Adding suffixes to words ending in 'fer'

1. Complete this table by adding **ed** and **ing** to the words in the boxes.

prefer

differ

offer

infer

	ed	ing
	....	....
	....	....
	....	....
	....	....

2. Underline the word in **bold** that has the correct ending in each sentence.

Melanie (**defered** / **deferred**) taking her driving test until the following year.

Izzy's dog was (**suffering** / **sufferring**) from a poorly paw.

Avani couldn't tell the (**difference** / **differrence**) between Spanish and Italian.

3. Some of the words in the passage below are spelt incorrectly.
Circle the incorrect words and write the correct version of each word in the box below.

*During the competition, contestants were not allowed to speak to one another
– confering was forbidden. The referree was very strict about this. Participants
were allowed to make notes, and many were seen refering to these. But
anyone caught cheating sufferred terrible consequences – all their points were
transfered to the other team and they had to do an embarrassing forfeit.*

conferring

Section 3 is finished! There's only one more thing to
do – tick the last tick box for this section. Done!

© CGP — not to be photocopied

Section 3 — Word Endings

Section 4 — Confusing Words

The soft c sound

The soft c sound is one that sounds like an 's'. Here's some handy spelling pract<u>ice</u>.

1. Tick the words below which have the soft c sound.

    ice ☐   calm ☐   lettuce ☐   knock ☐   excellent ☐

    city ☐   crack ☐   prince ☐   decide ☐   backpack ☐

    Choose two of the words you have ticked and use them in a sentence.

    ....

2. Circle the words that are spelt incorrectly.
    Then write the correct spelling of each incorrect word in the box.

    (fase)   price   sinema   parcel

    romanse   consert   ambulance   special

    pieses   burst   dice   applianse

face

3. The words in **bold** are incorrect. Write the correct spellings on the lines.

    I'm not very good at **pronounsing** words in French.   ....

    Rebecca has all the **nesessary** equipment.   ....

    My sister got a new **trisicle** for her birthday.   ....

    The church often smells of **incence** after the service.   ....

<u>Nice</u> work! Those soft c words can be tricky little things.
Tick the last box if you're a <u>successful</u> Spellasaurus.

Words with que in

1. Complete this table by filling in the missing **que** words.

Word	Clue
_ _ _ _ _ l c h	a sound made by boots sticking in mud
f r _ _ _ _ _ _ t _ _	a word meaning 'often'
s _ _ _ _ z _	to grip something tightly
s _ _ _ _ l	the next book or film in a series
o p _ _ _ _ _	the opposite of transparent

2. Fill in the blanks in this passage with **que** words.

    The knights would be leaving on their _ _ _ s _ at dawn the next day. They were

    going to try to c _ _ _ _ _ _ r the islands to the north of the kingdom. That

    night, the king and q _ _ _ _ _ threw a huge b _ _ _ _ _ _ t in the great hall.

    Before long, hundreds of people were _ _ _ _ _ n g up to get inside.

3. Add que to the letters in the box to make **que** words.

    ....*unique*.........   ....

    ....

    ....

    ....

grotes	
	bouti
stion	
~~uni~~	asy
che	
techni	ry

Have 'que' words left you <u>squealing</u> with delight,
or do you need to <u>squeeze</u> in some more practice?

© CGP — not to be photocopied   *Section 4 — Confusing Words*

Noun -ce / Verb -se

Some words have annoyingly similar spellings, but there are often rules to make them easier. The rule on this page is '-ce means the word is a noun, and -se means it's a verb'.

1. Circle all the nouns below and underline the verbs.

licence   device   advise

devise   license   practice

advice   practise

2. Match up each sentence with the correct word to fill the gap.

I .... you not to enter the lion enclosure.

I've invented a new nose-picking ....

I always ask my Aunt Kat for fashion ....

Our coach will .... a full training plan.

device

devise

advice

advise

3. Underline the correct spelling to complete each sentence below.

Sita has violin (**practice** / **practise**) every other day.

You need a special (**licence** / **license**) to get into the building.

4. Write each of these words in a sentence.

advise ....

practise ....

licence ....

device ....

Have you earned your Spellasaurus <u>licence</u>? Tick a box to show how much more <u>practice</u> you need.

© CGP — not to be photocopied

ei and ie words

You can use this chart-topping rhyme to help with ei and ie words:
'i' before 'e' except after 'c', if the vowel sound rhymes with bee.

1. Write the ie and ei words into the correct parts of the table below.

	rhymes with bee	doesn't rhyme with bee
after c		
not after c	*retrieve*	

retrieve   ancient

ceiling   freight

deceive   thief

sufficient   height

grief   vein

2. Finish each word by adding either **ie** or **ei**.

sh.....ld   **sl.....gh**   **conc.....ve**   **sc.....nce**

misch.....f   **br.....fly**   **w.....gh**   **perc.....ve**

Choose one of the words from above and use it in a sentence.

....

3. Choose the correct spellings from the words in the box to complete these sentences.

The .... for losing is wearing pyjamas to school.

Will was so .... to find his lost cat, Sir Sleepalot.

Tamara is very .... in the mornings.

I .... the prize for the most stuck-out belly button.

relieved	
	forfeit
forfiet	
	efficient
releived	
	recieved
received	
	efficeint

'ie' and 'ei' words are no match for a Spellasaurus.
Tick one of the boxes to show how you're getting on.

Comparatives and superlatives

Comparatives compare two things, and superlatives describe 'the most' of something.

1. Fill in the gaps in these sentences using the words in the box.

> **high**   **higher**   **highest**

Our block of flats is .... than my friend Rachel's.

You have to bungee jump from a very .... platform.

Mount Everest is the .... mountain in the world.

2. Complete these rows of adjectives, comparatives and superlatives.

scary	➡	....	➡	....
....	➡	noisier	➡	....
....	➡	....	➡	gentlest

3. Change each of these words into a **comparative**.

great ....   **clever** ....

rich ....   **lazy** ....

wet ....   **early** ....

4. Change this word into a **superlative** and use it in a sentence.

heavy ....

Spellasauruses are the <u>brainiest</u> of all dinosaurs.
Are you one of them? Tick a box and let's see.

Unstressed letters

1. This word search contains **nine** words with unstressed letters. Write them in the box.

C	H	O	C	O	L	A	T	E	F	D
O	U	N	D	F	B	K	C	D	A	I
M	L	E	R	F	S	Z	A	Q	C	F
P	C	O	I	E	P	J	L	A	T	F
A	A	M	N	R	Q	F	E	K	O	E
N	E	N	U	I	C	Z	N	X	R	R
Y	W	E	D	N	E	S	D	A	Y	E
O	T	R	Z	G	W	X	A	I	H	N
E	Y	J	A	N	U	A	R	Y	E	C
F	S	E	C	T	O	R	H	G	N	E

2. Complete the words in these sentences by writing in the unstressed letters.

    The army gen......ral didn't realise his jacket was tucked into his underwear.

    My dad is always trying to get me to eat more veg......tables.

    My favourite subject is g......ography, but I also like hist......ry.

    We had to look for the book in the ref......rence section of the libr......ry.

    I wasn't concentrating because I was so desp......r......te for the loo.

3. Each of these words has one incorrect vowel. Circle the error, and write the correction.

    an(a)mal ➡ ...i...   poisun ➡ ....   consonont ➡ ....

    prudict ➡ ....   inturest ➡ ....   miserible ➡ ....

    origanal ➡ ....   lituracy ➡ ....   marvillous ➡ ....

Don't stress — practice makes perfect with this lot.
Are you a Spellasaurus yet? Time to tick a progress box.

© CGP — not to be photocopied   *Section 4 — Confusing Words*

Silent letters

1. Draw lines to match the words with the silent letters they contain.

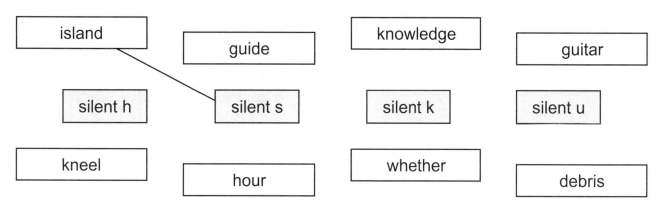

island		knowledge	
	guide		guitar
silent h	silent s	silent k	silent u
kneel		whether	
	hour		debris

2. Finish each word by adding the silent letter.

......nickers ......riggle spag......etti colum......

cas......le disg......ise bom...... forei ......n

3. Complete the words in these sentences by writing the missing silent letter.

Quentin was excited to be a g.....est at Buckingham Palace.

James always asks for extra g.....erkins on his burger.

Daniel has finished the desi.....n for his ten-minute ice cream machine.

Mrs Tickington had to call out a plum.....er to fix the shower yet again.

4. Tick the words below which have silent letters.

comb ☐   numb ☐   patrol ☐   detail ☐   ghastly ☐

eat ☐   hello ☐   young ☐   spade ☐   whistle ☐

Choose one of the words you have ticked and use it in a sentence.

....

Silent letters

5. Use the clues to complete the crossword. All the words contain a silent letter.

Across

1. A car has four of these.
5. The season after summer.
6. To speak very quietly.
7. To sound like another word.

Down

1. The plastic around a sweet.
2. A baby sheep.
3. The past tense of 'to know'.
4. How you get up a ladder.

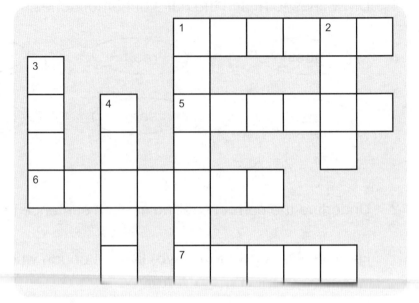

6. Fill in the gaps in these sentences using the words in the box.

choir	guide	scheme	Christmas	hymns	writes

Gran lives in Canada, so she .... us a letter at ....

We mostly sing .... in our church ....

My dad has set up a new .... to train .... dogs.

7. Write each of these words in a sentence.

wrist ....

building ....

baguette ....

Even silent letters can't sneak up on a Spellasaurus.
Are you ready to take them on in the SAT? Tick a box.

Homophones

Homophones are words that sound the same, but have different meanings and spellings.

1. Draw lines to match the pairs of homophones.

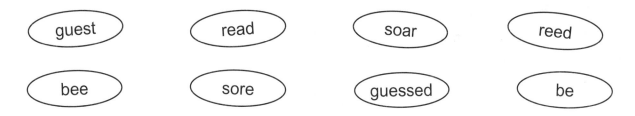

| guest | read | soar | reed |

| bee | sore | guessed | be |

2. Underline the correct spelling in each sentence below.

Hamish wants (**to** / **too** / **two**) live in London when he's older.

I have one pet snake and (**to** / **too** / **two**) crocodiles.

Rowena put (**to** / **too** / **two**) much salt in the fish stew.

3. Write each of these words in a sentence.

there ....

their ....

they're ....

4. Use pairs of homophones to complete these pairs of sentences.

a. I couldn't see in the m __ s __ .   I tried to catch it but I m __ s __ __ __ .

b. We've just s __ e __ a spaceship.   He painted a country s c __ __ __ __ .

c. I was so b __ r __ __ __ in maths today.   Miss Smith wrote on the b __ __ r __ .

d. I bought a p __ i __ of shoes.   Flik ate a p __ a __ with her lunch.

          © CGP — not to be photocopied

Homophones

5. Replace the underlined words with the correct homophone.

There is a big difference in <u>wait</u> between <u>mail</u> and female polar <u>bares</u>.

The <u>breaks</u> have rusted on my <u>blew</u> bike, so Dad is going to <u>bye</u> me a new <u>won</u>.

6. **Nine** of the words in the passage below are incorrect.

Circle the incorrect words and write the correct homophones in the box below.

> *Roberto, the groom, stood nervously at the alter. Suddenly, the church doors opened, and Roberto spotted Anna at the other end of the isle. "She looks beautiful," he side. He felt rather outdressed in his plane black suit, but he new Anna wouldn't mined at all. They had bean weighting four this day for years.*

7. Write a homophone of each of these words.

seam	➡	....

paws	➡	....

threw	➡	....

hare	➡	....

oar	➡	....

know	➡	....

Dastardly things, homophones, but not enough to fox a Spellasaurus. How did you get on with these pages?

© CGP — not to be photocopied   *Section 4 — Confusing Words*

Tricky words

1. Circle all the correct spellings in the box below.

disappoint shoulder explaination furthermore reherse
marraige fether variety protien should

2. These words are spelt incorrectly. Write the corrections on the lines.

newsance ⟹ .... **Britian** ⟹ ....

caractar ⟹ .... **ankor** ⟹ ....

extintion ⟹ .... **attatch** ⟹ ....

3. Write each of these words in a sentence.

necessary ....

serious ....

fascinated ....

4. The words in the box are spelt incorrectly.
   Use the corrected spellings to fill the blanks in the passage below.

conseqwences	combineing	cayos	mischievious	immediatly

Bella had been very __ __ __ __ __ __ __ __ __ __ __ __ . She'd caused __ __ __ __ __

in the bathroom, __ __ __ __ __ __ __ __ __ __ all of her mum's perfumes and shampoos

together. Sadly, her mum realised __ __ __ __ __ __ __ __ __ __ __ __ , and sent Bella

to her room. Bella knew there would be further __ __ __ __ __ __ __ __ __ __ __ __ __ __ .

    © *CGP — not to be photocopied*

Tricky words

5. Draw a circle around the word that has been spelt incorrectly in each sentence. Write the correct spelling on the line.

It's sometimes difficult to (guage) the weather. ....*gauge*...............

We're having a celebration for my Gran's fifieth birthday. ....

A chameleon can camuoflage itself in any environment. ....

My sister has a tendency to exagerate her stories. ....

At school we've been practising our discriptive writing. ....

My teddy isn't particularaly special, but I love him anyway. ....

6. Complete this table by filling in the missing letters.

Word	Clue
_ _ _ _ _ _ _ _ _	you often see this when you hear thunder
_ _ _ _ _ _ _ _ _ _	a picture taken with a camera
_ _ _ _ _ _ _	the organ in your mouth used for tasting
_ _ _ _ _ _ _ _ _ _	the name for things like pens, pencils and rulers
_ _ _ _ _ _ _ _ _	a percussion instrument played with mallets
_ _ _ _ _ _ _	something that needs solving; rhymes with 'history'
_ _ _ _ _ _ _ _ _ _	a book that tells you the meanings of words

Wow, you've reached the end of the book! Are you feeling like a mighty Spellasaurus? Tick a final box.

© CGP — not to be photocopied   1114 - 12674   *Section 4 — Confusing Words*

More brilliant SAT Busters for KS2 Maths and English...

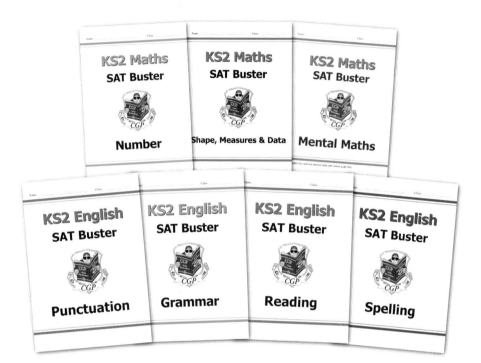

KS2 Maths SAT Buster — Number

KS2 Maths SAT Buster — Shape, Measures & Data

KS2 Maths SAT Buster — Mental Maths

KS2 English SAT Buster — Punctuation

KS2 English SAT Buster — Grammar

KS2 English SAT Buster — Reading

KS2 English SAT Buster — Spelling

...have you got yours?

See them all at www.cgpbooks.co.uk
— or ask your teacher for more info!

Do not use while feeding lions

ISBN 978 1 78294 278 8

9 781782 942788

E6S221   £3.95
                (Retail Price)

www.cgpbooks.co.uk

KR-920-865